The Lady with the Alligator Purse

Illustrated by Mervyn Pywell

HOUGHTON MIFFLIN COMPANY

BOSTON

ATLANTA   DALLAS   GENEVA, ILLINOIS   PALO ALTO   PRINCETON

I had a little brother,

his name was Tiny Tim,

I put him in the bathtub

to teach him how to swim.

He drank up all the water,

he ate up all the soap,

he had to go to bed

with a bubble in his throat.

Mom called the doctor,

Dad called the nurse,

I called the lady

with the alligator purse.

In came the doctor,

in came the nurse,

in came the lady

with the alligator purse.

"Mumps," said the doctor,

"Measles," said the nurse,

"Soap!" said the lady

with the alligator purse.

"Penicillin," said the doctor,

"Castor oil," said the nurse,

"Ice cream!" said the lady

with the alligator purse.

Out went the doctor,
out went the nurse,
out went the lady
with the alligator purse.